UNFORGETTABLE

PIANO SOLOS

Great Music from the Movies

CW01023322

Wise Publications
London / New York / Paris / Sydney / Copenhagen / Madrid

Exclusive Distributors:
Music Sales Limited
8/9 Frith Street,
London W1V 5TZ, England.
Music Sales Pty Limited
120 Rothschild Avenue,
Rosebery, NSW 2018,
Australia.

Order No. AM950796
ISBN 0-7119-7055-6
This book © Copyright 1998 by Wise Publications

Music compiled by Peter Evans
Book design by Pearce Marchbank, Studio Twenty, London
Computer layout by Ben May

Printed in the United Kingdom by
Redwood Books Limited, Trowbridge, Wiltshire.

Your Guarantee of Quality
As publishers, we strive to produce every book to the highest
commercial standards. This book has been carefully designed to
minimise awkward page turns and to make playing from it a real
pleasure. Particular care has been given to specifying acid-free,
neutral-sized paper made from pulps which have not been
elemental chlorine bleached. This pulp is from farmed sustainable
forests and was produced with special regard for the environment.
Throughout, the printing and binding have been planned to ensure a
sturdy, attractive publication which should give years of enjoyment.
If your copy fails to meet our high standards, please inform us
and we will gladly replace it.

Music Sales' complete catalogue describes thousands of titles
and is available in full colour sections by subject, direct from
Music Sales Limited. Please state your areas of interest and
send a cheque/postal order for £1.50 for postage to:
Music Sales Limited, Newmarket Road,
Bury St. Edmunds, Suffolk IP33 3YB.

Visit the Internet Music Shop at
http://www.musicsales.co.uk

A Man And A Woman (Un Homme Et Une Femme)

Original Words by Pierre Barouh. English Lyric by Jerry Keller
Music by Francis Lai.

Dmaj7

C#7

Cmaj7

F#m7   B7   Emaj7

Emaj7   Dm7   G7♭9   Cmaj7   Dm7

G7   C6   F#m7   B7   Emaj7

Em7   A7   Dmaj7

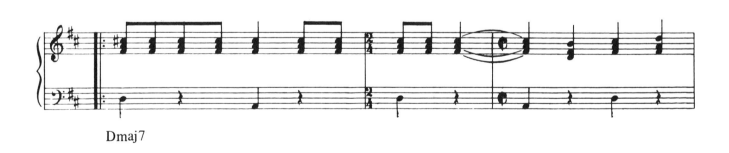

Dmaj7

C#7

Cmaj7

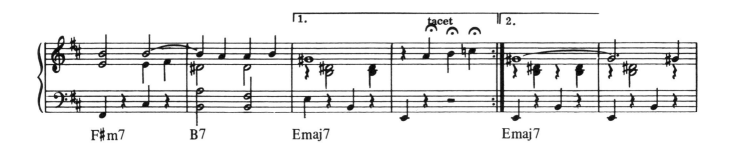

F#m7   B7   Emaj7   Emaj7

F# m 7   B7   Emaj7   F#m7

Emaj7   Emaj7 Ebmaj7 Dmaj7

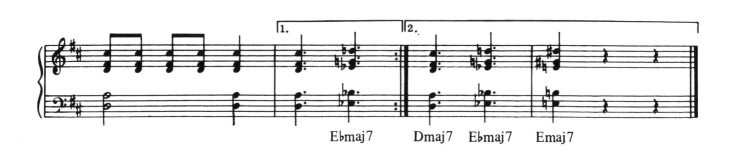

Ebmaj7   Dmaj7 Ebmaj7 Emaj7

All The Things You Are

Music by Jerome Kern
Words by Oscar Hammerstein II

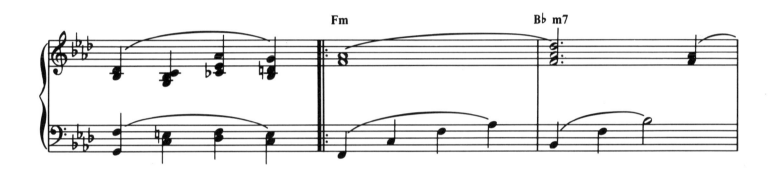

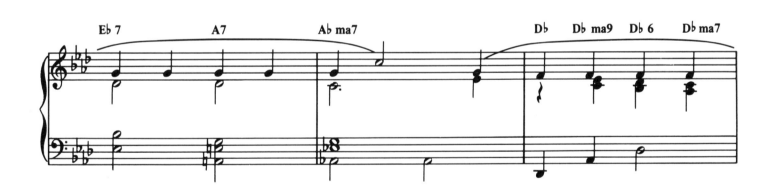

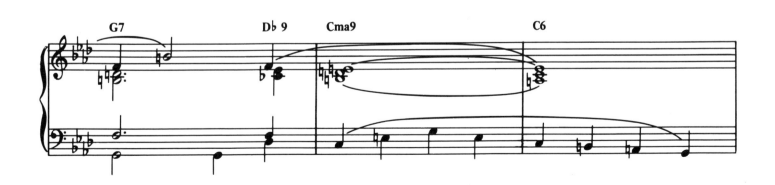

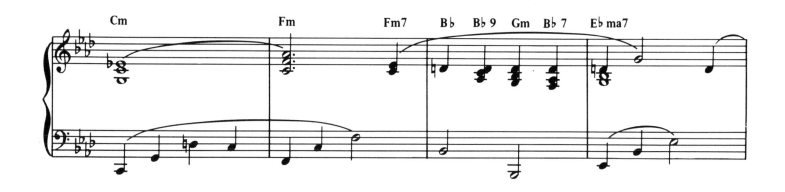

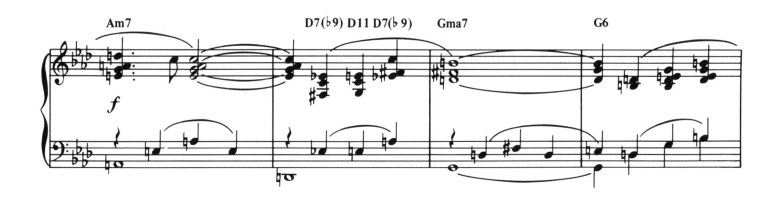

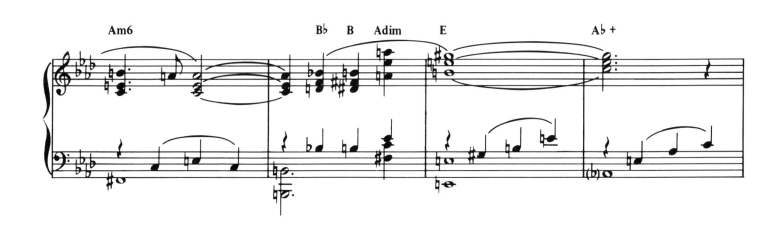

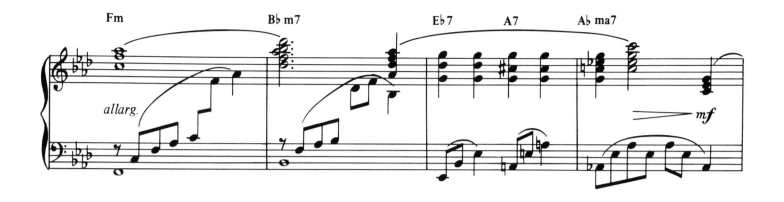

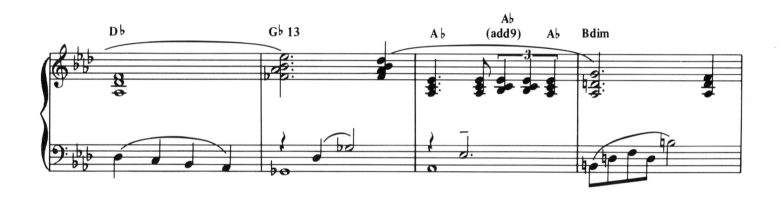

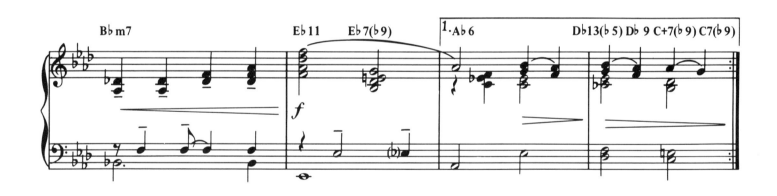

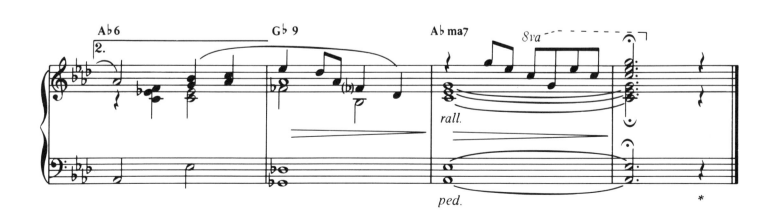

But Not For Me

Music & Lyrics by George Gershwin & Ira Gershwin

Rather slow (smoothly)

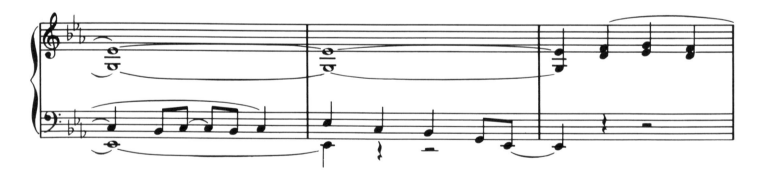

Charade

Words by Johnny Mercer
Music by Henry Mancini

15

Don't Cry For Me Argentina

Music by Andrew Lloyd Webber
Lyrics by Tim Rice

E7   A   D   * Ped   *

Ped   *mf*

Ped sim.
G/D   A7/D

D   Bm/D

E7   E/D   A/C♯   E7

Refrain

Slow tango feel

A   D

17

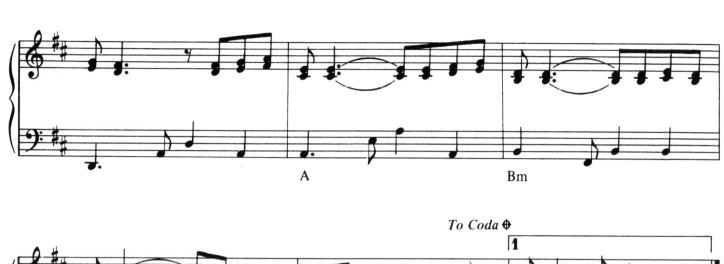

A   Bm

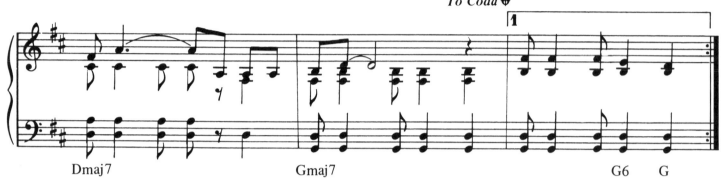

To Coda ⊕

1

Dmaj7   Gmaj7   G6   G

2 *Freely*

Gmaj7   F♯m7

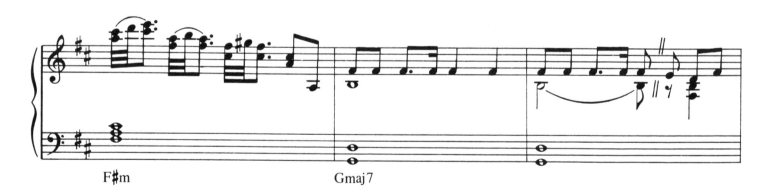

F♯m   Gmaj7

D.%. al Coda

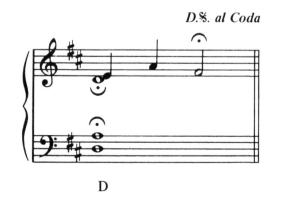

D

⊕ *CODA*

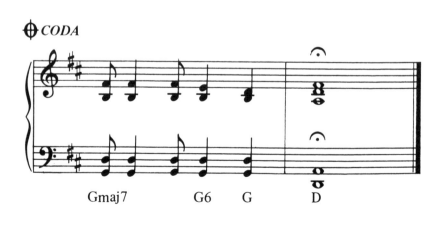

Gmaj7   G6   G   D

I Don't Know How To Love Him

Music by Andrew Lloyd Webber
Lyrics by Tim Rice

In The Cool, Cool, Cool Of The Evening

Music by Hoagy Carmichael
Words by Johnny Mercer

I Will Wait For You

Words by Normal Gimbel
Music by Michel Legrand

26

Lawrence Of Arabia

By Maurice Jarre

29

Maria

Music by Leonard Bernstein
Lyrics by Stephen Sondheim

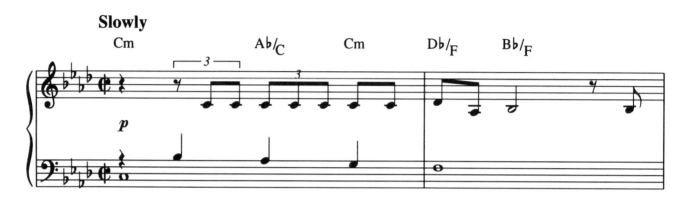

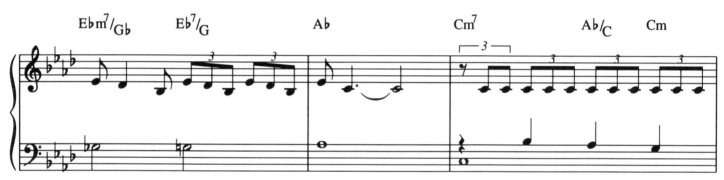

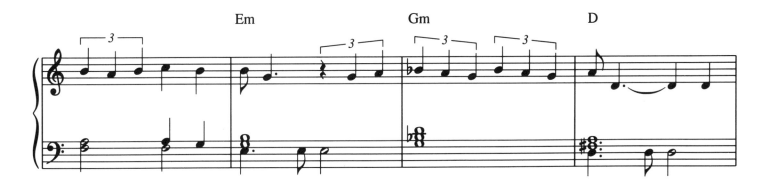

rall.

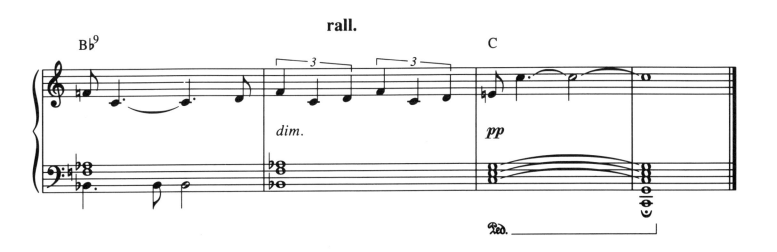

Once In A Lifetime

Words & Music by Leslie Bricusse & Anthony Newley

Schindler's List

By John Williams

Expressively

Singin' In The Rain

Words by Arthur Freed
Music by Nacio Herb Brown

39

Smile

Words by John Turner & Geoffrey Parsons
Music by Charles Chaplin

Bb   Eb9   Bb

Bbdim   Cm   Fdim Cm7   G7   G11 G7   Cm

Ab7   Bb

Gm   Cm7   F13(b9)

D   G7   D

41

42

Smoke Gets In Your Eyes

Music by Jerome Kern
Words by Otto Harbach

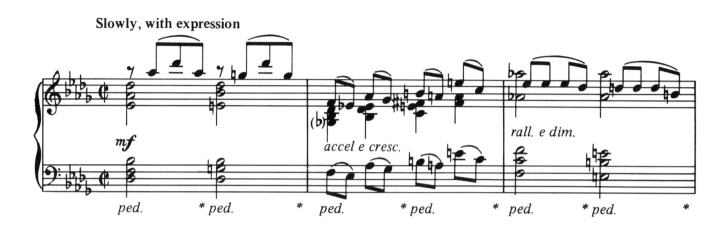

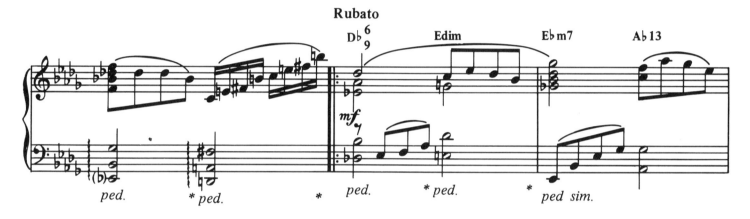

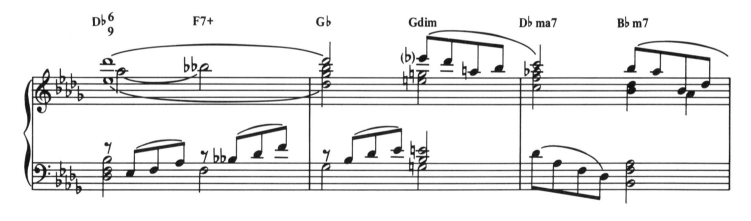

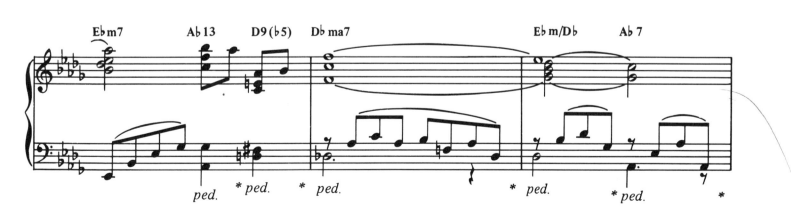

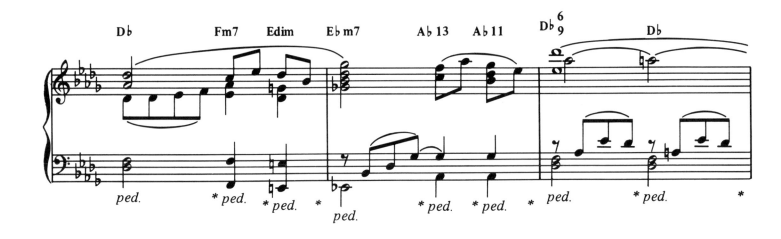
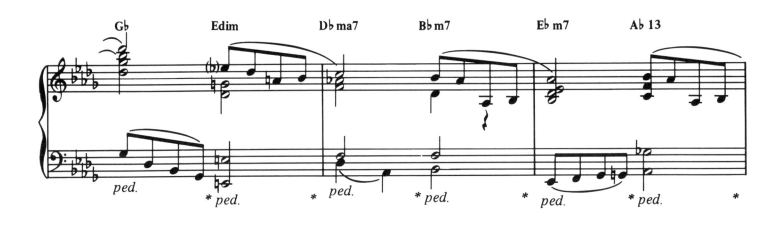
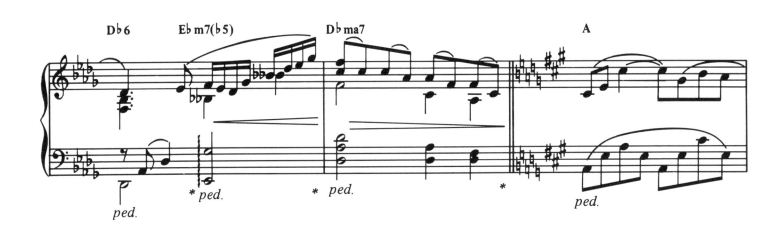
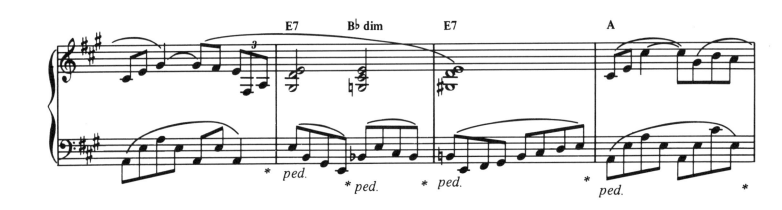

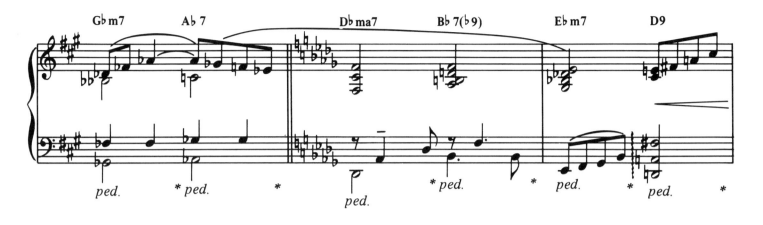

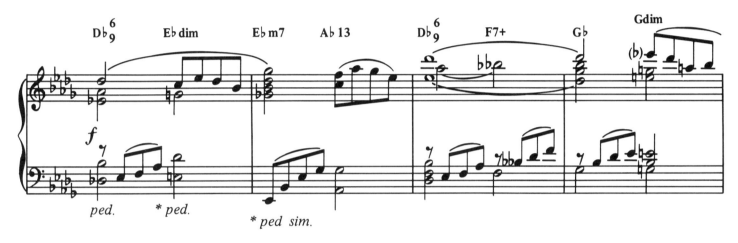

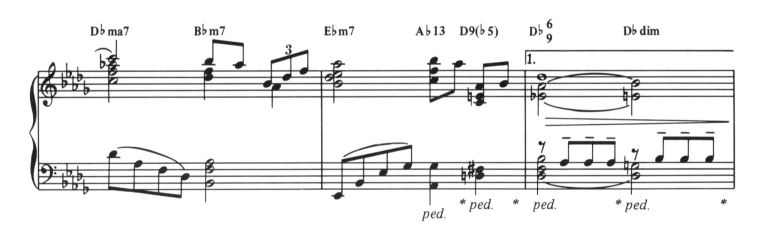

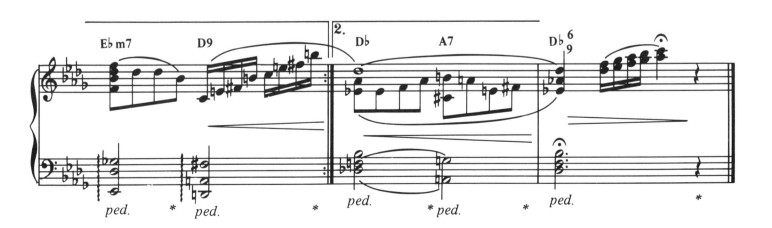

Speak Softly Love

Music by Nino Rota
Words by Larry Kusik

Somewhere

Music by Leonard Bernstein
Lyrics by Stephen Sondheim

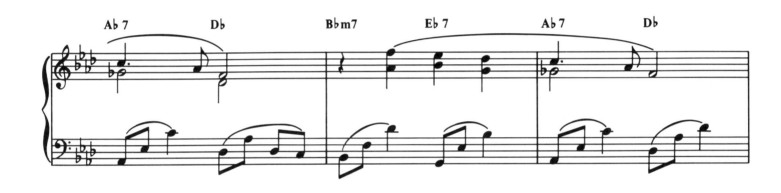

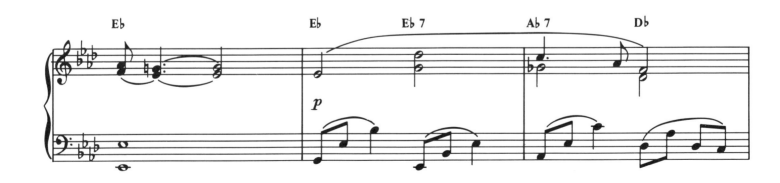

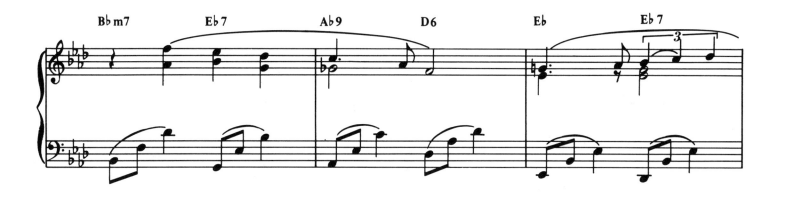

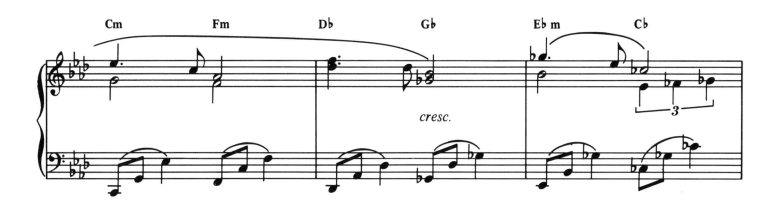

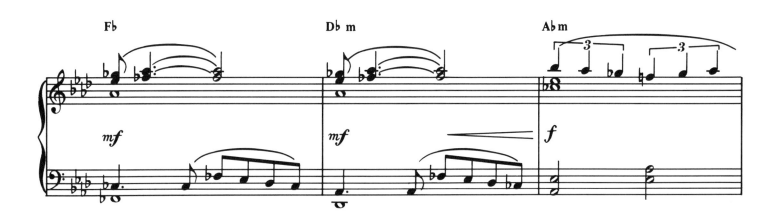

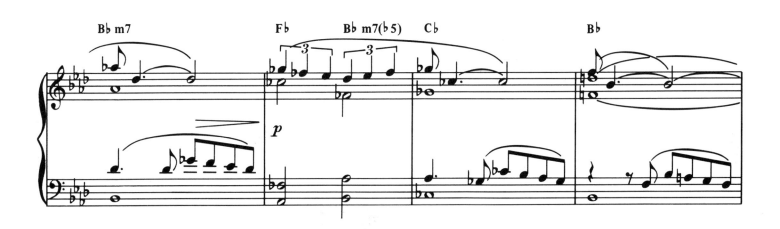

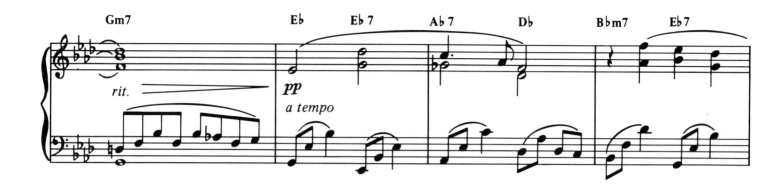

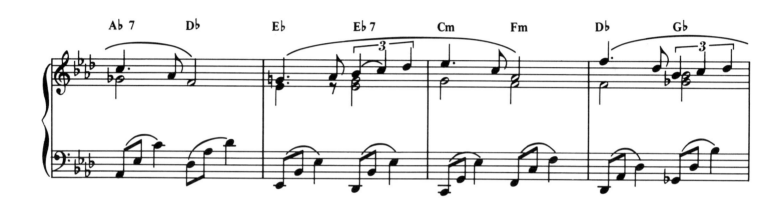

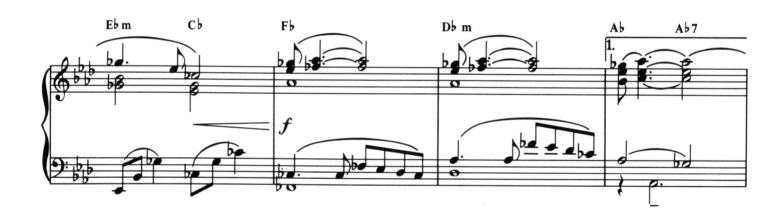

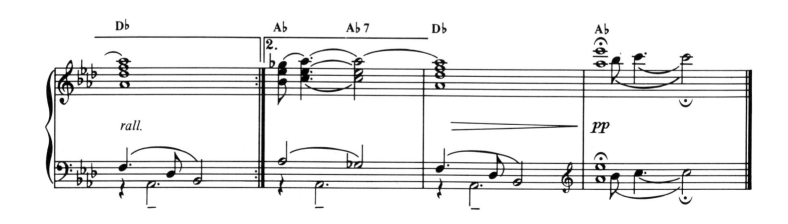

Summertime

By George Gershwin, Ira Gershwin, DuBose & Dorothy Heyward

That Old Black Magic

Music by Harold Arlen
Words by Johnny Mercer

Moderately bright

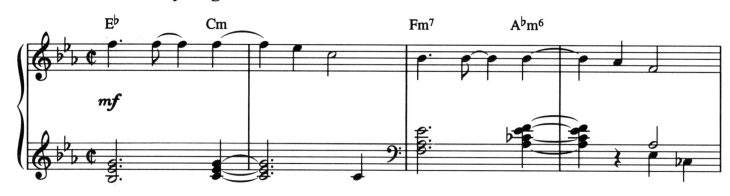

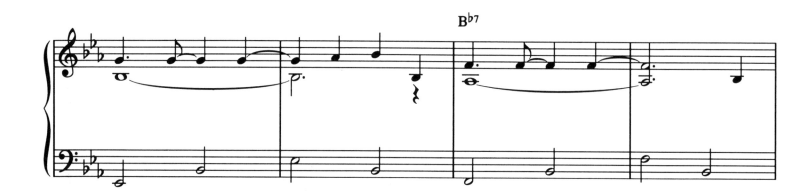

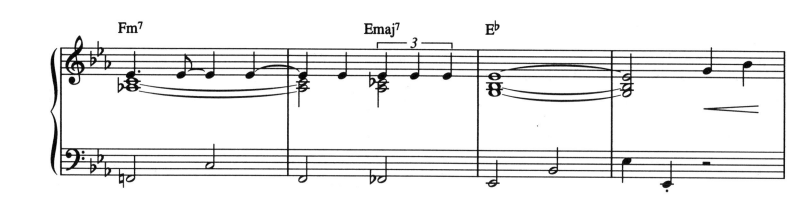

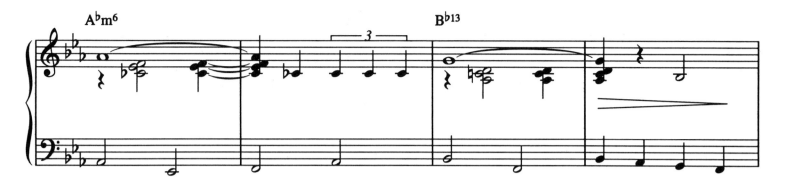

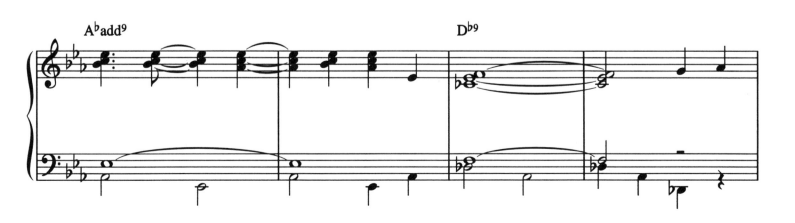

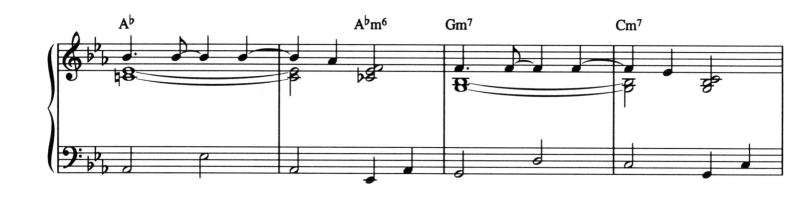

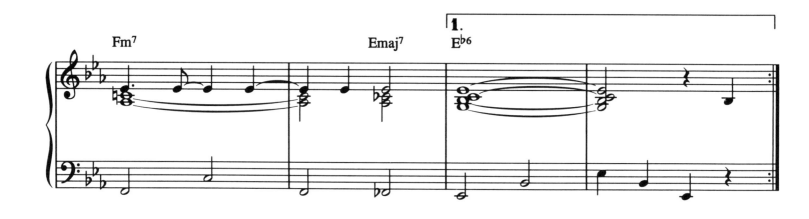

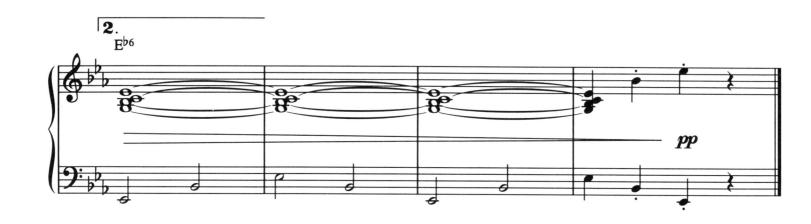

The Entertainer

By Scott Joplin

61

The Shadow Of Your Smile

Words by Paul Francis Webster
Music by Johnny Mandel

63

The Song From Moulin Rouge (Where Is Your Heart)

Words by William Engvick
Music by Georges Auric

Unchained Melody

Words by Hy Zaret
Music by Alex North

Moderately slow

Where Do I Begin

Music by Francis Lai
Words by Carl Sigman

Slowly

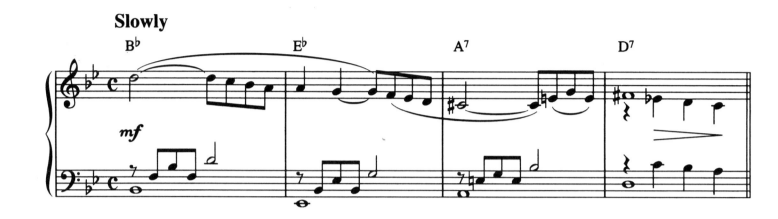

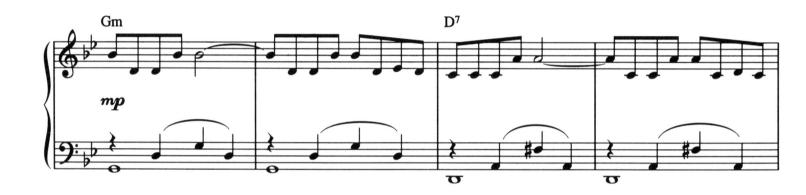

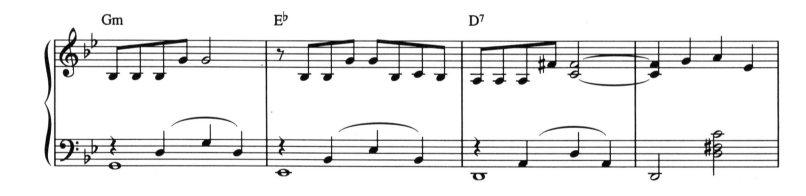

71

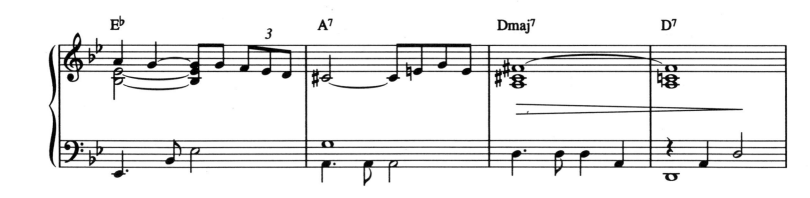

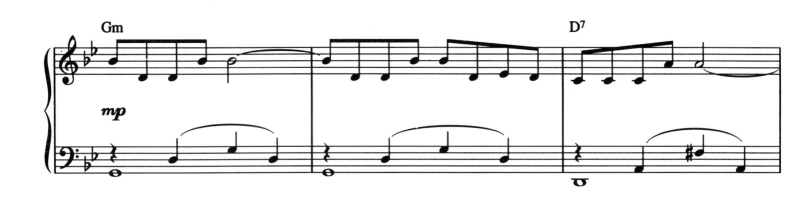

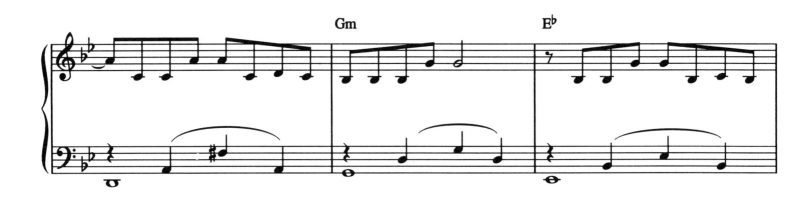

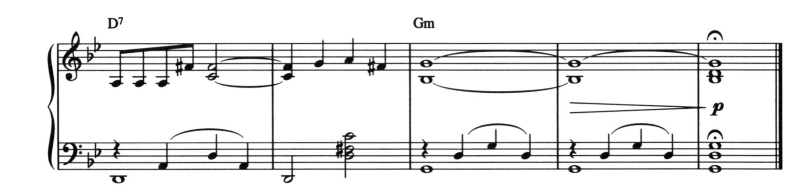

You Light Up My Life

Words & Music by Joe Brooks

© COPYRIGHT 1976 BIG HILL MUSIC, USA.
EMI MUSIC PUBLISHING LIMITED, 127 CHARING CROSS ROAD, LONDON WC2.
ALL RIGHTS RESERVED. INTERNATIONAL COPYRIGHT SECURED.

73

Younger Than Springtime

Words by Oscar Hammerstein II
Music by Richard Rodgers